UKULELE
FINGERSTYLE
Mastery

TERRY CARTER

UKELIKE THEPROS

UKE LIKE THE PROS

CONTENTS

ISBN-13: **978-1-7359692-0-6**

Copyright 2020

TERRY CARTER
UKELIKETHEPROS**.COM**

THE ESSENTIALS

It is important to learn and memorize these terms and symbols because they not only applay to ukulele but to all music.

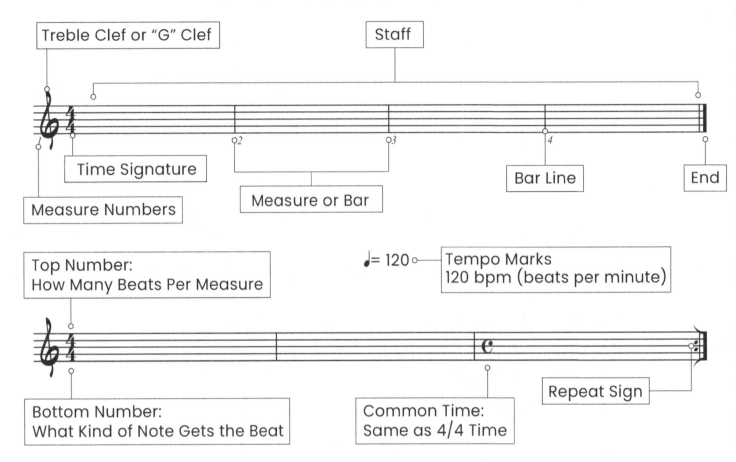

Treble Clef or "G" Clef · Staff · Time Signature · Measure Numbers · Measure or Bar · Bar Line · End

Top Number:
How Many Beats Per Measure

♩= 120 Tempo Marks
120 bpm (beats per minute)

Bottom Number:
What Kind of Note Gets the Beat

Common Time:
Same as 4/4 Time

Repeat Sign

Notes On The Staff: There are seven notes in music (A, B, C, D, E, F, G) and they move up and down alphabetically on the staff.

G A B C D E F G A B C D E F G A B C D E F

How To Remember The Notes:

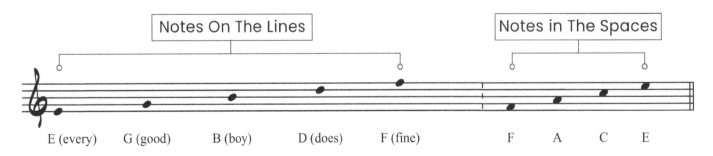

Notes On The Lines

Notes in The Spaces

E (every)   G (good)   B (boy)   D (does)   F (fine)   F   A   C   E

HOW TO READ TAB

Tablature (TAB) is a form of music reading for Ukulele that has been around for a long time. The TAB staff has 4 lines and each line represents a string on the ukulele. The number represent the fret you play on and are located on the string you play them on.

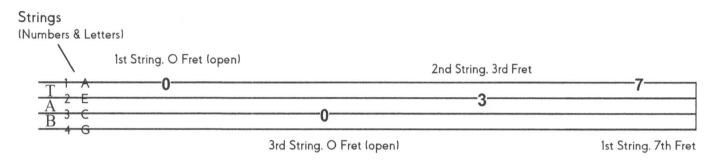

OPEN STRINGS ON THE UKULELE

These are the open string names for a soprano, concert, and tenor ukulele. The only difference between the High G and the Low G is that ukuleles with a Low G have a wider range of notes.

Open String Notes (Ukulele's with High G String):

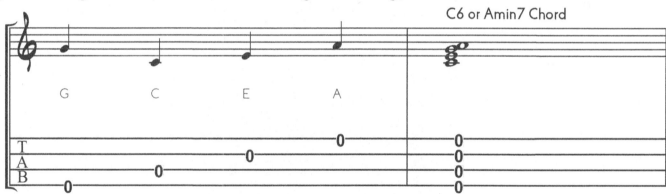

Open String Notes (Ukulele's with Low G String)

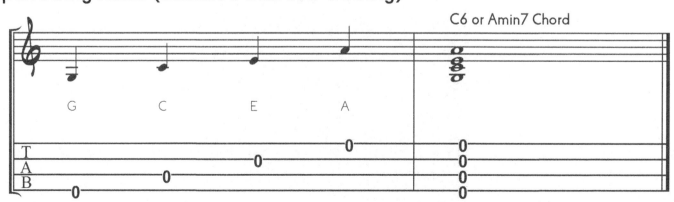

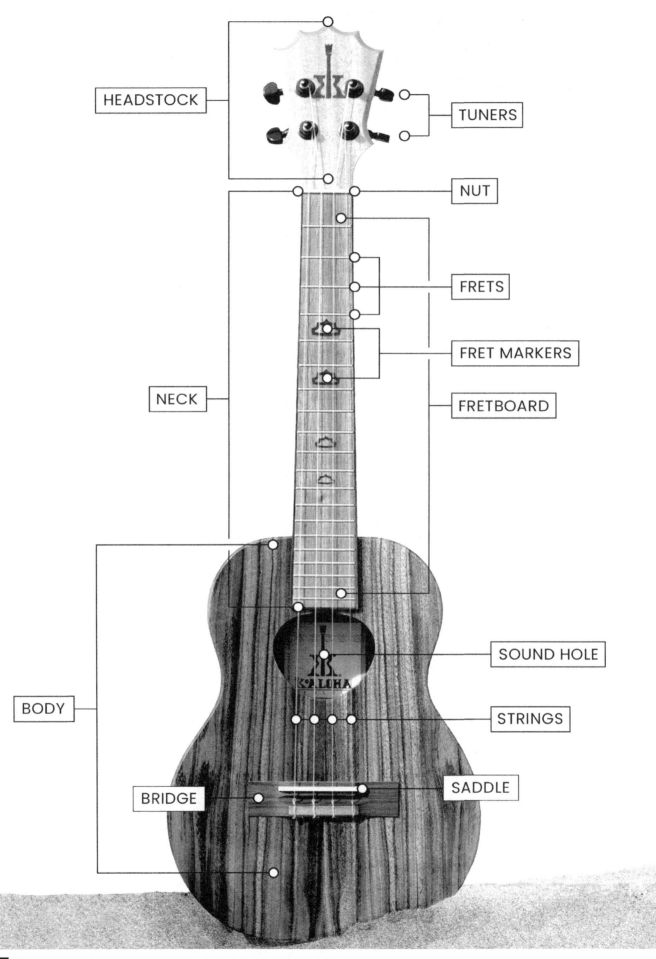

HEADSTOCK

TUNERS

NUT

FRETS

FRET MARKERS

NECK

FRETBOARD

SOUND HOLE

BODY

STRINGS

BRIDGE

SADDLE

NOTES ON THE UKULELE NECK

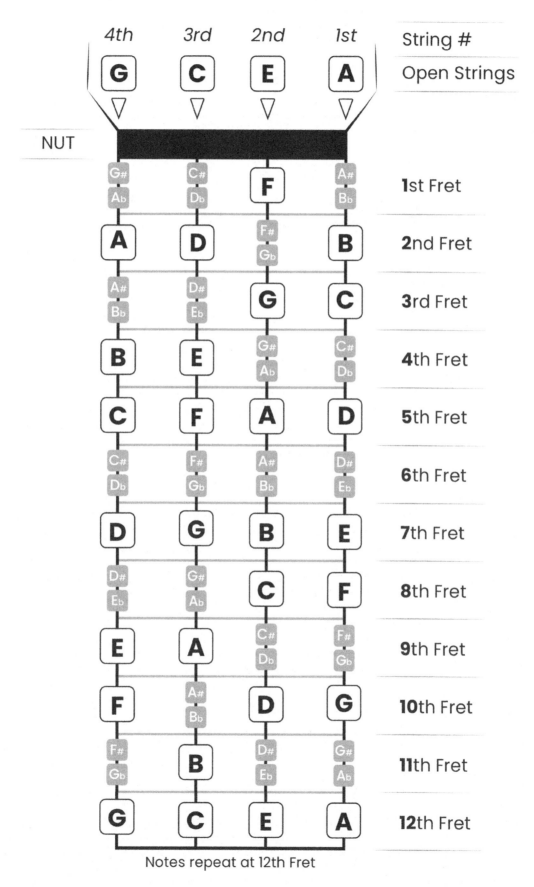

Notes repeat at 12th Fret

MUSIC SYMBOLS TO KNOW

A variety of symbols, articulations, repeats, hammer on's, pull off's, bends, and slides.

Fermata: Hold note

Staccato: Play note short

Accent: Play note loud

Accented Staccato:
Play loud & short

Vibrato:
Rapid "shaking"
of note.

Arpeggiated Chord:
Play the notes in fast
succession from low
to high strings

Grace Note:
Fast embellishment
note played before
the main note

Mute:
"Muffle" sound of
strings either with
left or right hand

Down Stroke:
Pick string(s) with
an downward motion

Up Stroke:
Pick string(s) with
an upward motion

Tie:
Play first note but do
not play second note
that it is tied to

Ledger Lines:
Extend the staff
higher or lower.

Slash Notation:
Repeat notes &
rhythms from
previous measure

1 Bar Repeat:
Repeat notes &
rhythms from
previous measure

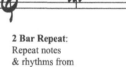

2 Bar Repeat:
Repeat notes
& rhythms from
previous 2 measures

Repeat Sign:
(Beginning)

Repeat Sign:
(End)

1st Ending:
Play this part the first time only

2nd Ending:
Play this part the second time

D.C. AL FINE - *D.C.* (da capo) means go to the beginning of the tune and stop when you get to **FINE**

D.C. AL CODA - *D.C.* means go to the beginning of the tune and jump to *Coda* ⊕ when you see this sign ⊕

D.S. AL FINE - *D.S.* (dal segno) means go to the *Sign* 𝄋 and stop when you get to **FINE**

D.S. AL CODA - *D.S.* means go to the *Sign* 𝄋 and jump to the *Coda* ⊕ when you see ⊕

Sim... - Play the same rhythm, strum pattern, or picking pattern as the previous measure

Etc... - Continue the same rhythm, strum pattern, or picking pattern as the previous measure

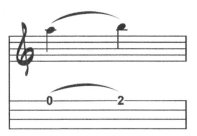

Hammer On:
Pick first note then hammer on to the next note without picking it.

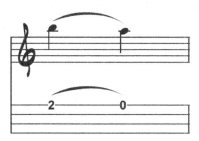

Pull Off:
Pick first note then pull off to the next note without picking it.

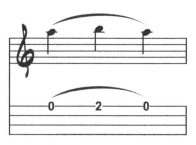

Hammer On & Pull Off:
Pick first note, hammer on to the next note and pull off to the last note all in one motion.

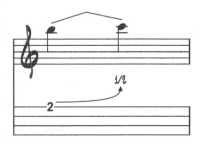

1/2 Step Bend:
Bend the first note a 1/2 step or 1 fret.

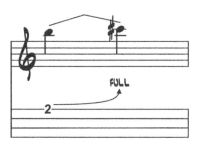

Whole Step Bend:
Bend the first note a whole step or 2 frets.

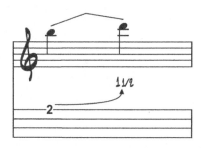

Step & 1/2 Bend:
Bend the first note 1 1/2 steps or 3 frets.

Forward Slide:
Pick first note and slide up to higher note.

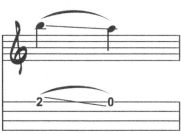

Backward Slide:
Pick first note and slide back to lower note.

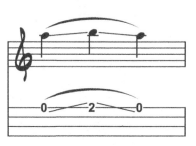

Forward/Backward Slide:
Pick first note, slide up to next note and then slide back.

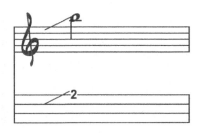

Slide Into Note:
Slide from 2-3 frets below note

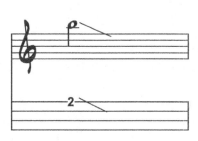

Slide Off Note:
Slide off 2-3 frets after note

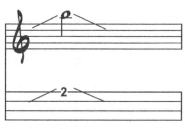

Slide Into Note then Slide Off Note

CHORD CHART

These are some of the most widely used chords in all of music. Although there are more chords than what is listed, these chords represent the most widely used shapes.

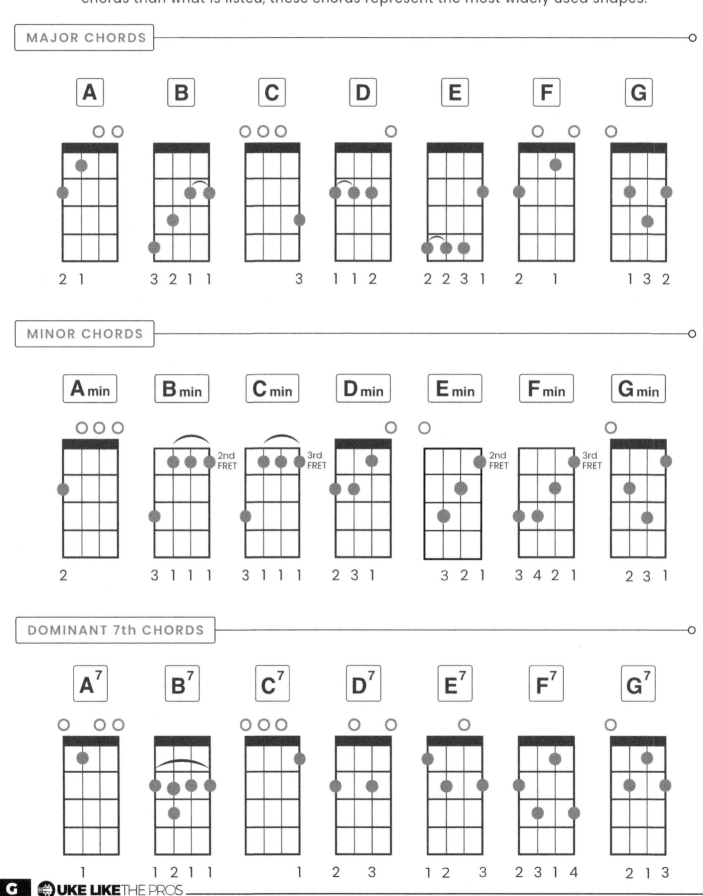

MAJOR 7th CHORDS

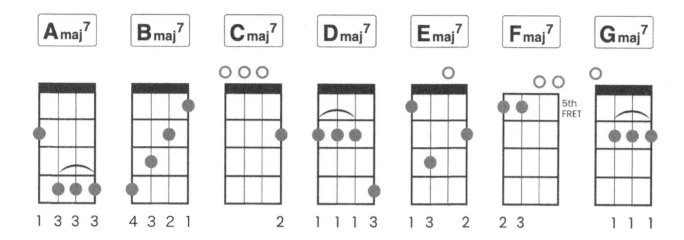

MINOR 7th CHORDS

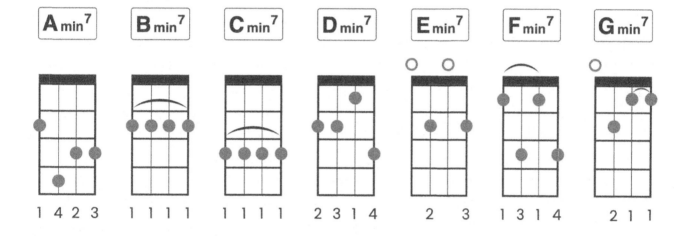

SUS + ADD CHORDS

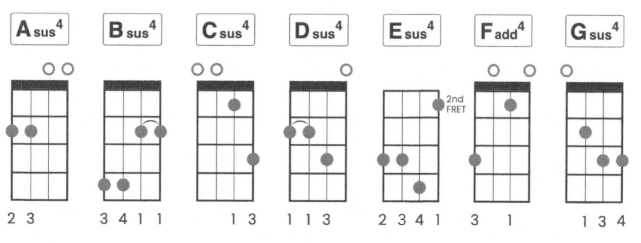

LESSON 01 **CASCADES** IN A MINOR

This fingestyle piece in A Minor uses the *p* (thumb), *i* (index), and *m* (middle) finger pattern
and can be played on low G or high G (low G preferred)

by Terry Carter

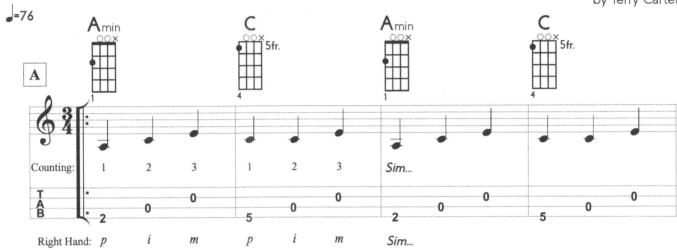

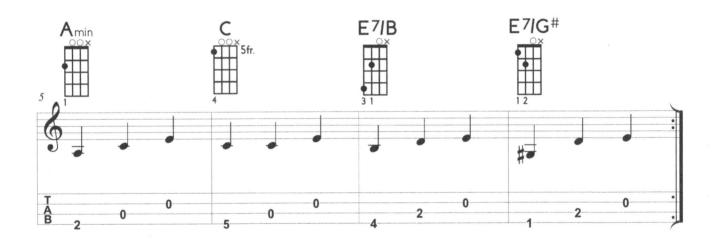

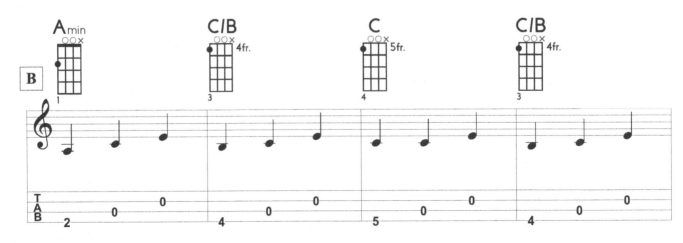

SOARING RAIN

IN C MAJOR

This fingestyle piece in C Major uses *pimi* finger pattern. *p* (thumb). *i* (index). *m* (middle) and *a* (ring). It can be played on low G or high G (low G preferred)

by Terry Carter

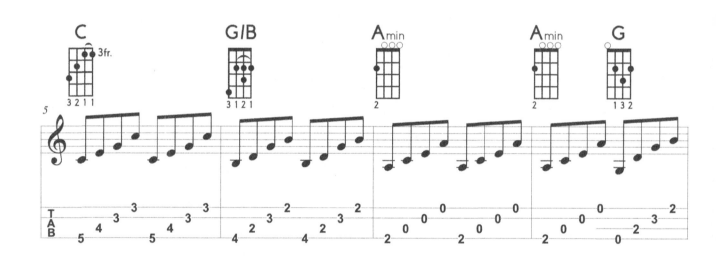

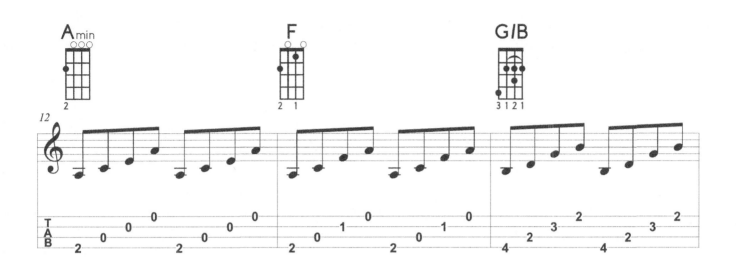

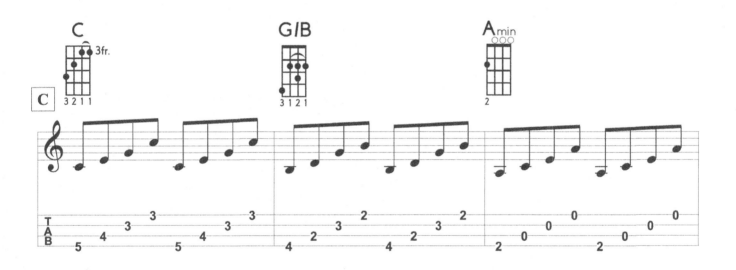

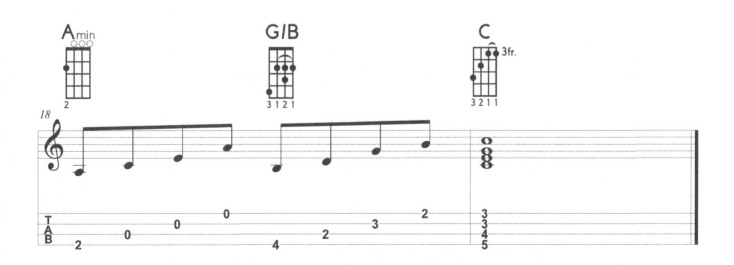

RISING TIDE

RISING TIDE IN C MAJOR

This fingestyle piece in C Major uses pimi finger pattern. p (thumb). i (index). m (middle) and a (ring). Notice how each chord has the C and G notes on the 1st and 2nd strings.

by Terry Carter

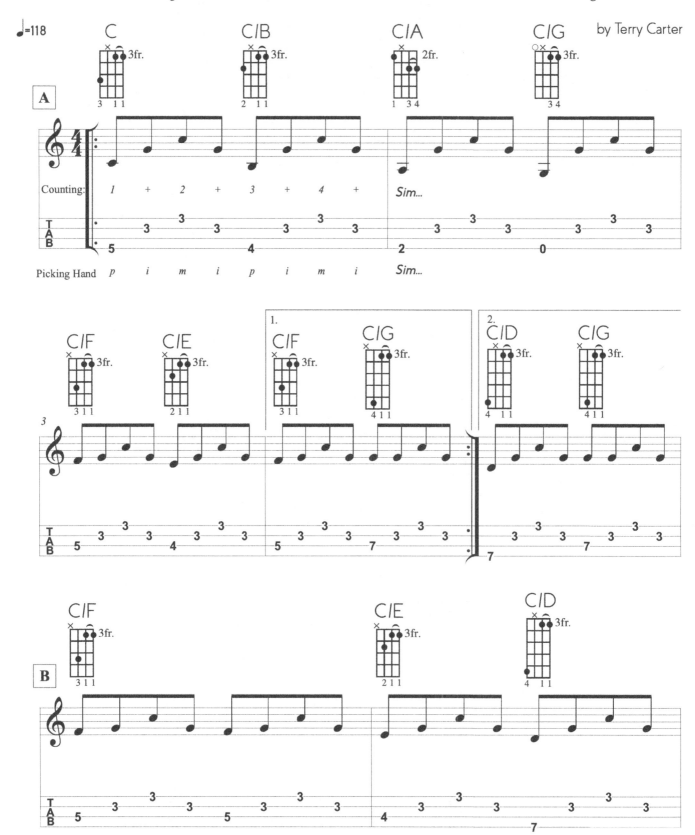

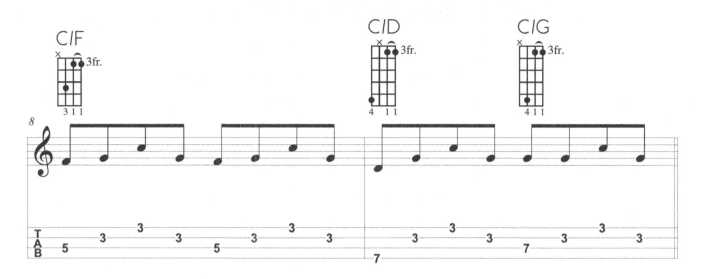

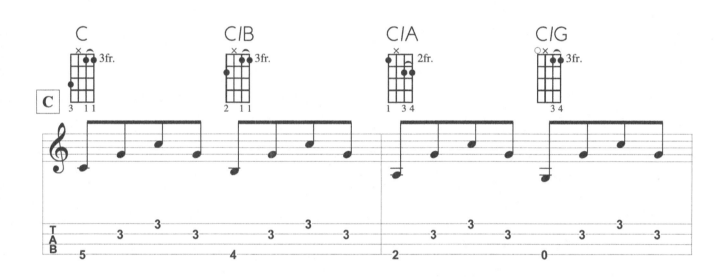

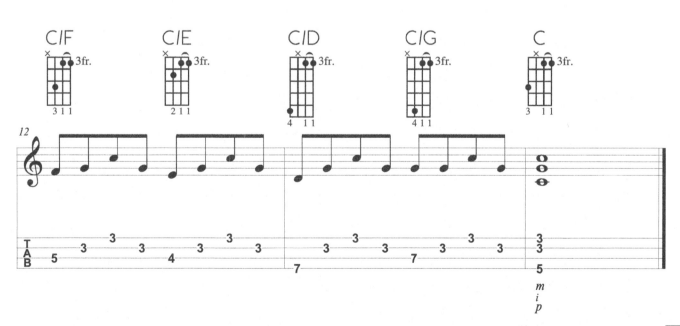

LESSON 04 **RED CROWN** IN A MINOR

This piece is in A Minor and uses a Low A on the 4th string. That means you have to turn your
4th string from G to A. Low G recommended

By Terry Carter

Tuning:
1 = A
2 = E
3 = C
4 = A

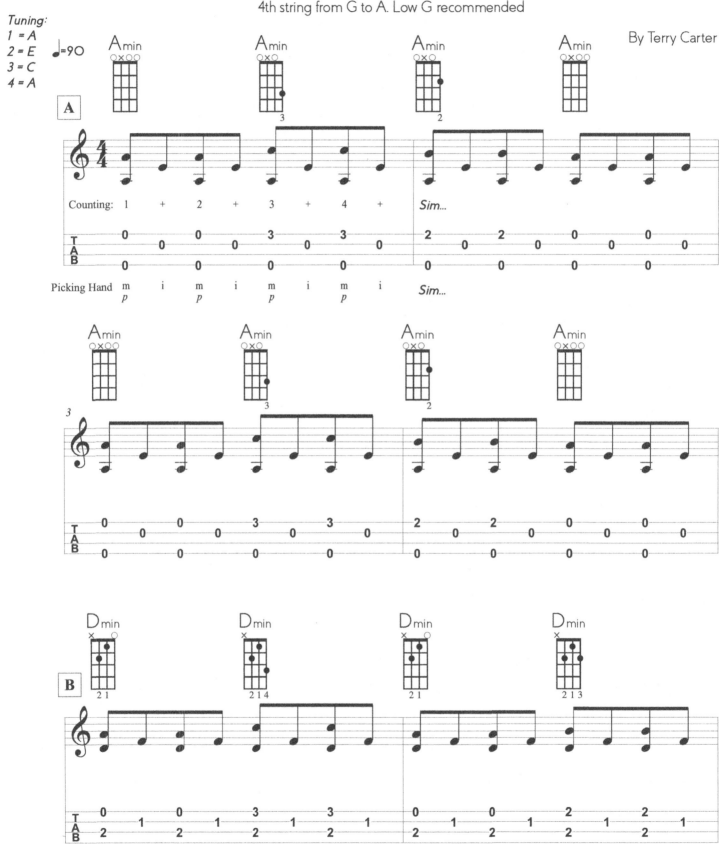

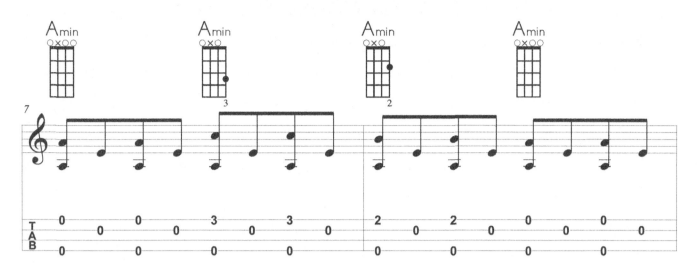

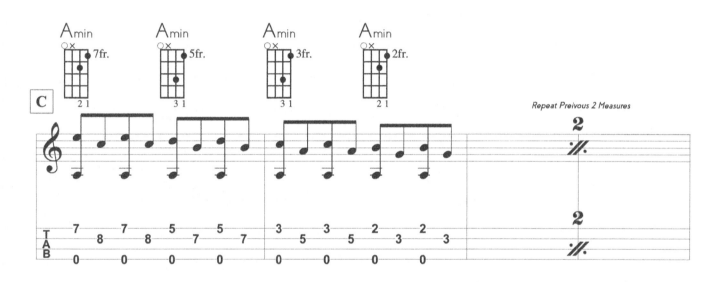

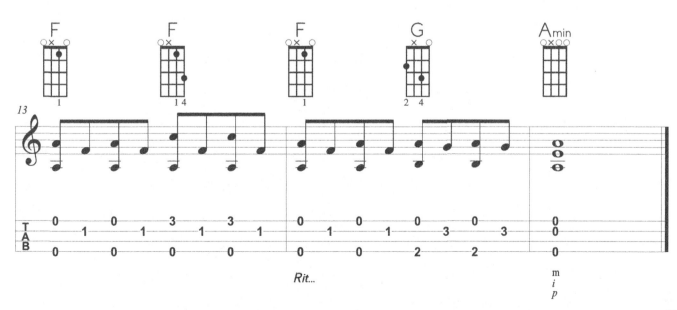

LESSON 05 **BETTER DAYS** IN C MAJOR

This piece is in C Major uses the thumb and a two finger pluck with the index and middle fingers.
Hopefully the sound of this song gives you hope for 'Better Days' ahead.

By Terry Carter

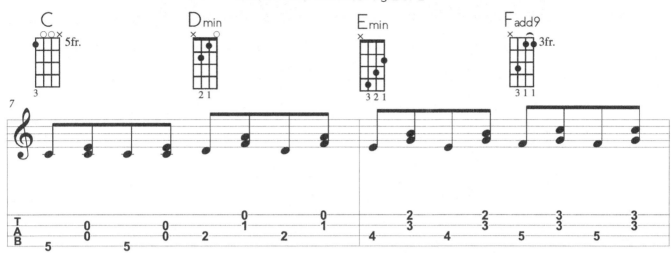

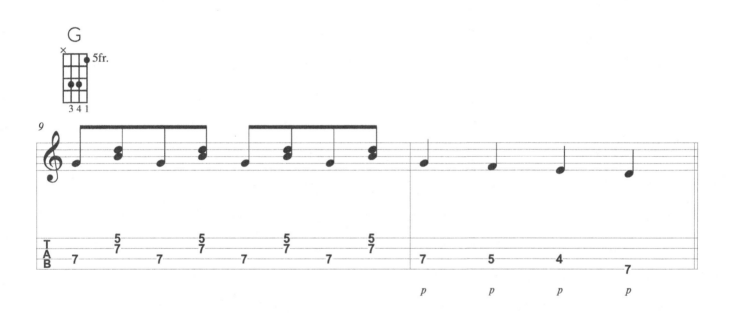

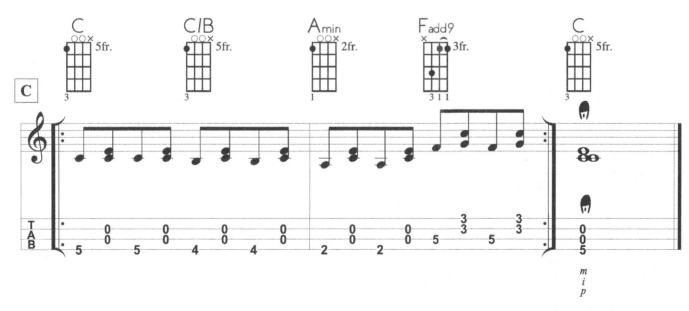

JASMINE NIGHTS IN G MINOR

This piece is in G Minor and uses the thumb and backward roll with the ring. middle. and index fingers. Backward rolls are when you go from higher strings to lowe strings.

By Terry Carter

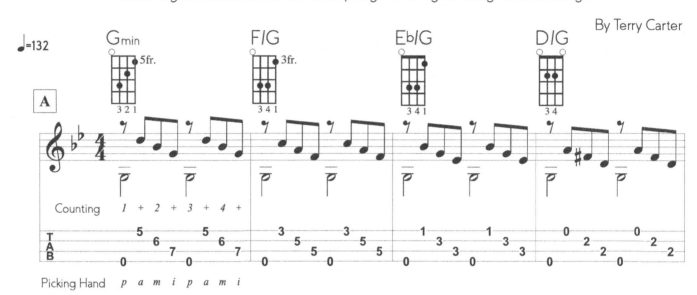

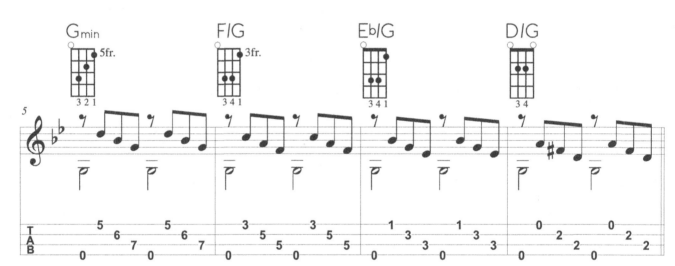

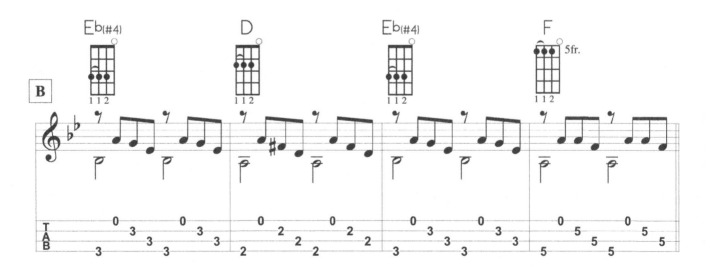

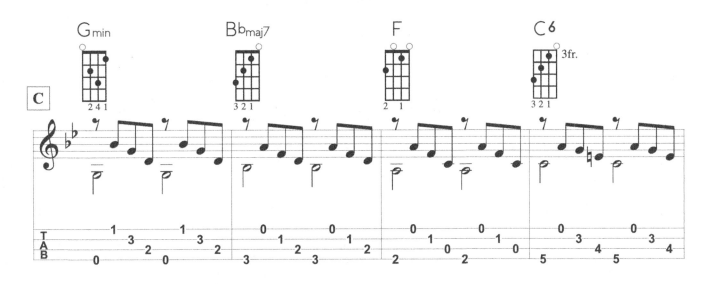

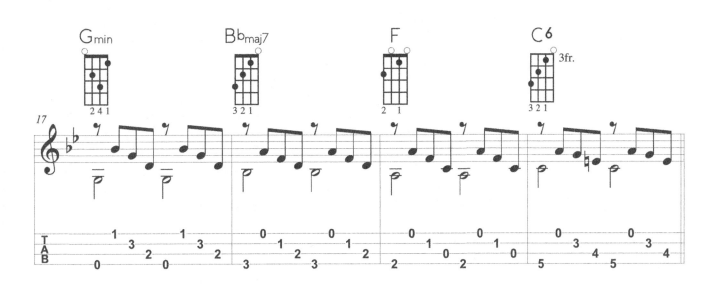

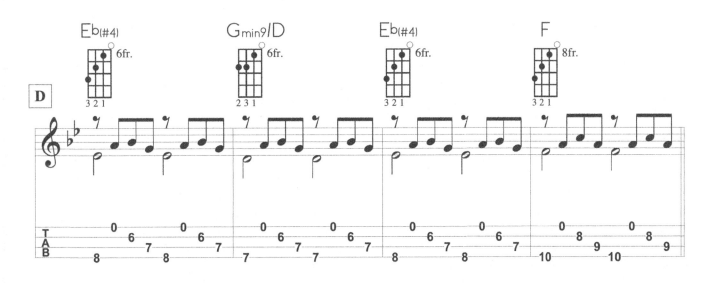

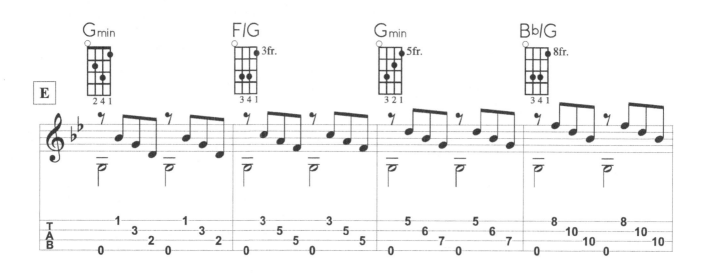

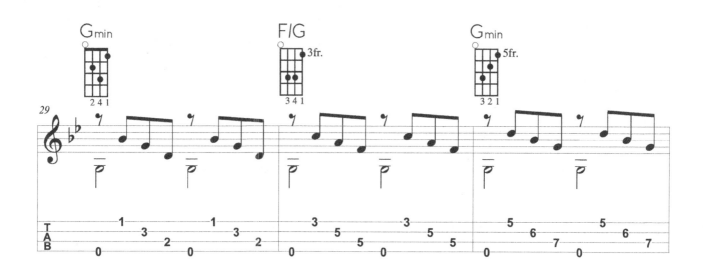

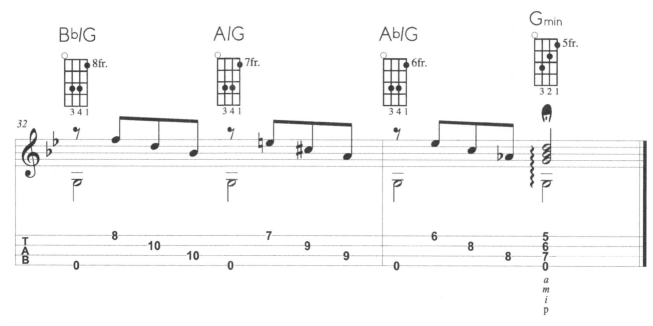

WHAT THE STUDENTS SAY:

I'm pretty new to the ukulele and am so happy
that I stumbled upon your website.
I've learned more in the last week of being a
Premium Member, than in the last few
months of trying to figure it out on my own
by watching YouTube!
I'm really enjoying your easy approach
and teaching style.

Thank you Terry. I appreciate that you are
making yourself accessible for all us newbies
with such rudimentary questions. And again,
thank you for offering such great, detailed, easy
to follow courses that even a no previous
musical knowledge total beginner like me can
understand and follow.

UKULELE STUDENT.

This piece is in C Major uses the thumb for the entire piece and sounds best on High G. Make sure to use a nice smooth and fluid strum to not only bring out the chords but accentuate the melody.

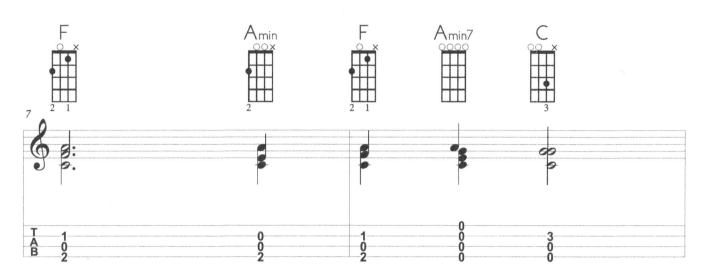

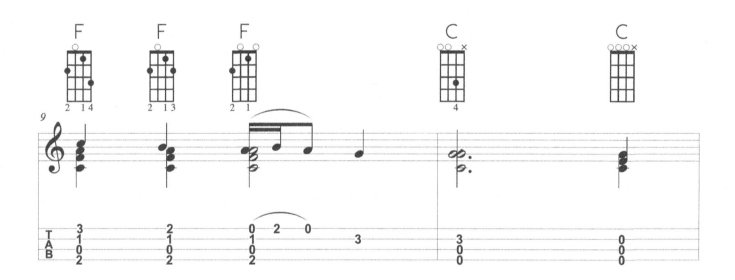

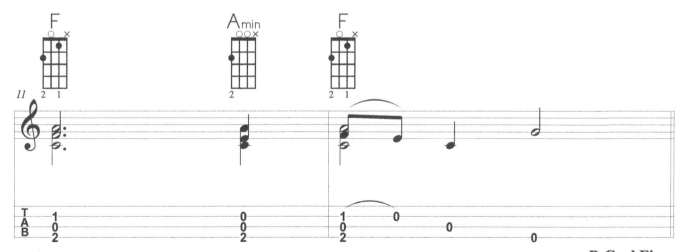

D.C. al Fine

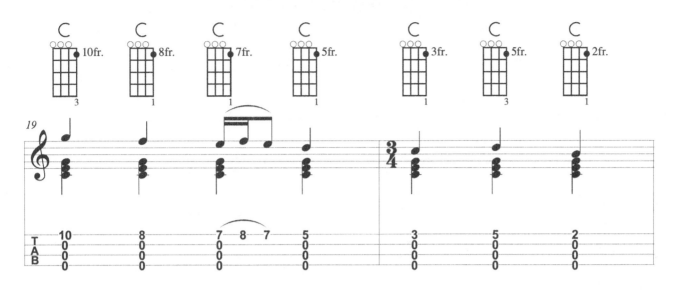

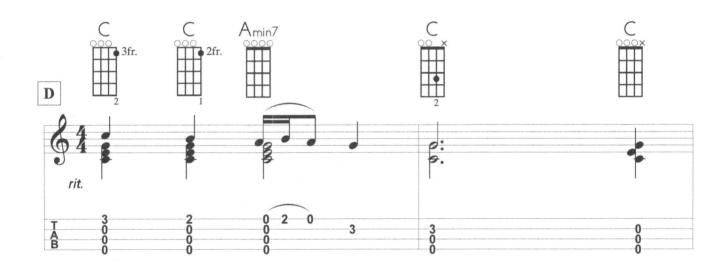

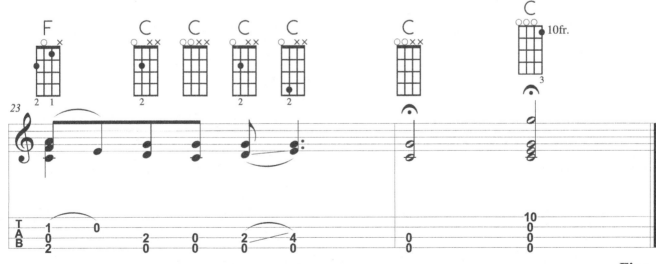

Fine

KAT'S BOUREE IN G MAJOR

This piece in G Major is in 6/8 time. counted 1 -2 -3 - 4 - 5 - 6 and uses a pinch between thumb (p) and ring (a) and a pluck between the index (i) and middle (m) fingers.

by Terry Carter

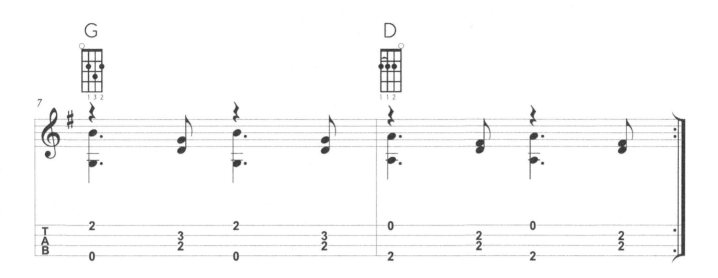

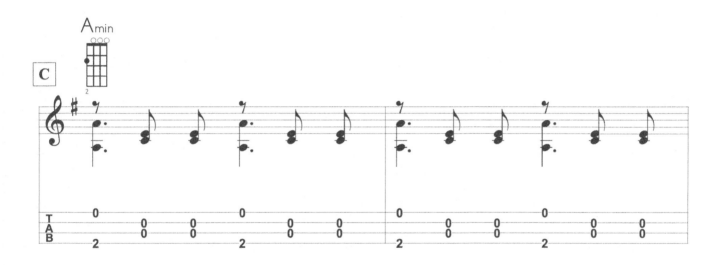

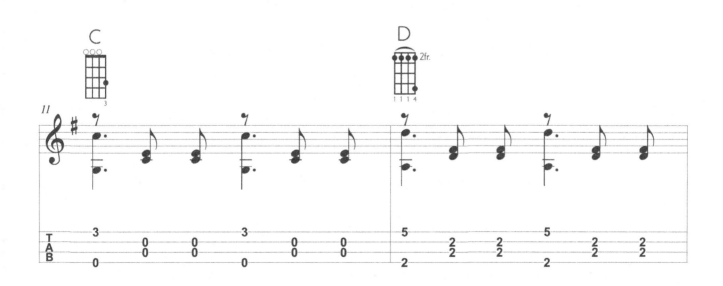

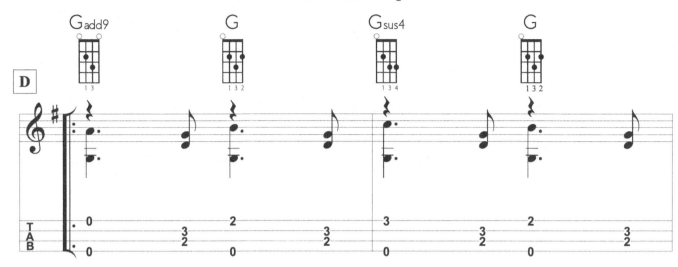

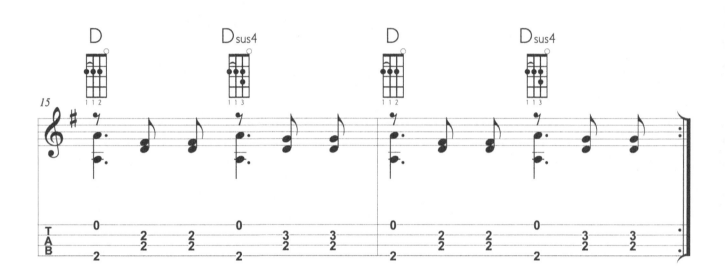

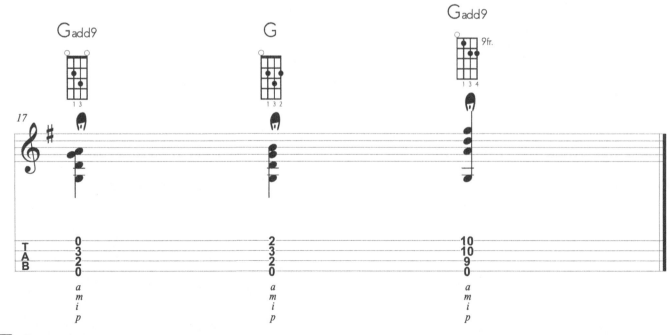

LOVER'S LAMENT IN D MINOR

This piece in D Minor uses a combination of chords and single notes. Play every chord with a fast arpeggiated rolll and play the single notes using classical style alternating i (index) and m (middle) fingers.

by Terry Carter

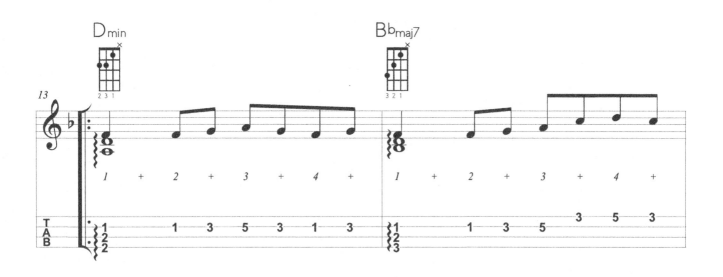

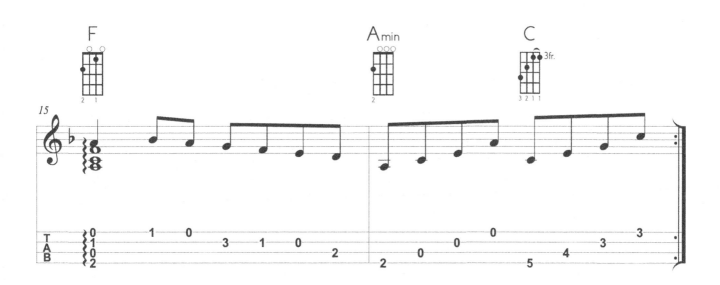

LESSON 10 MAUI BREEZE IN C MAJOR

This piece in C Major is a combination of pinches and arpeggios. Although any ukulele will work. I recommend using a high "G" for this piece.

By Terry Carter

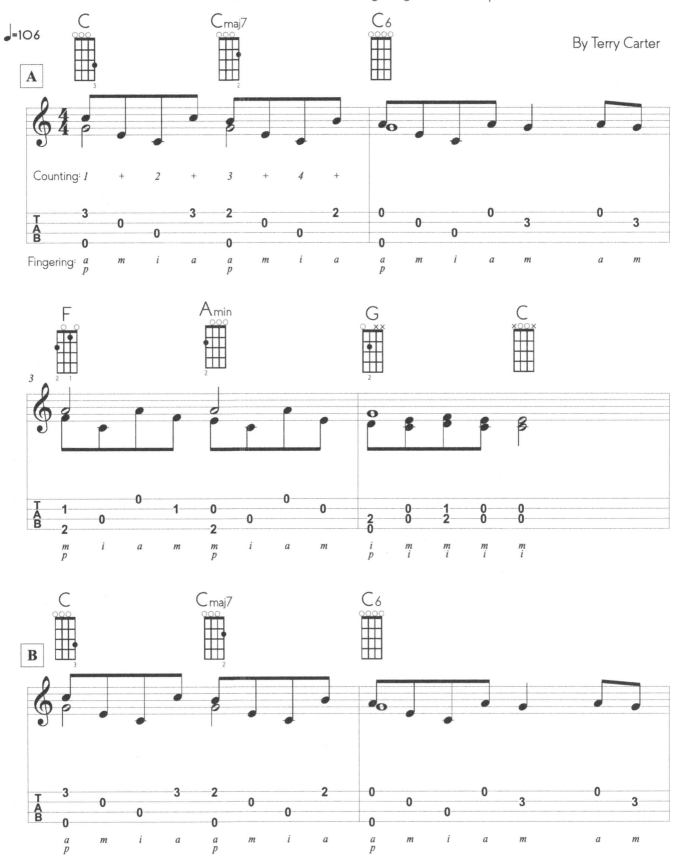

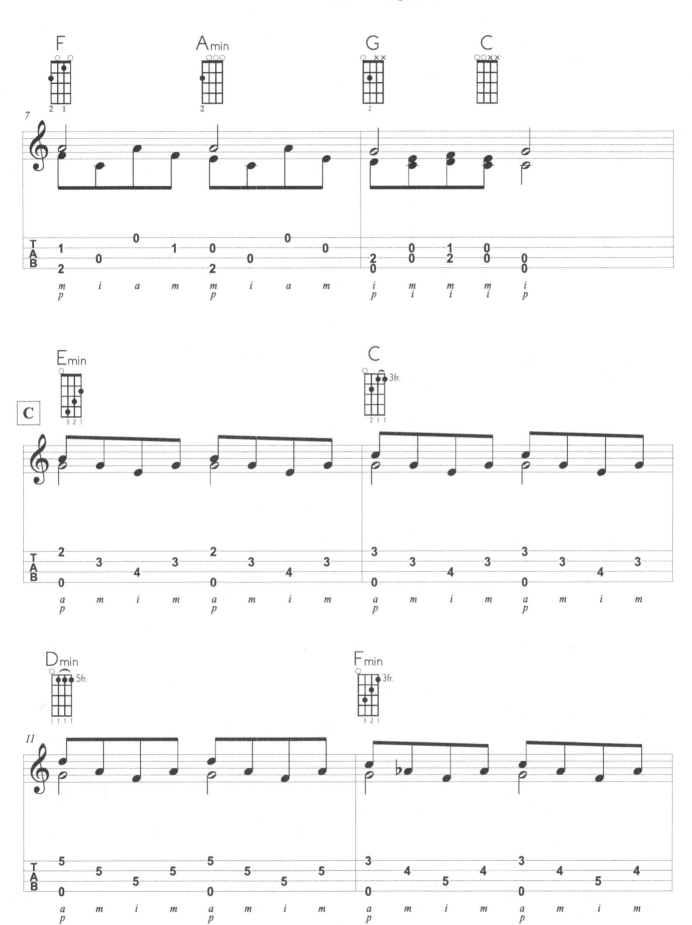

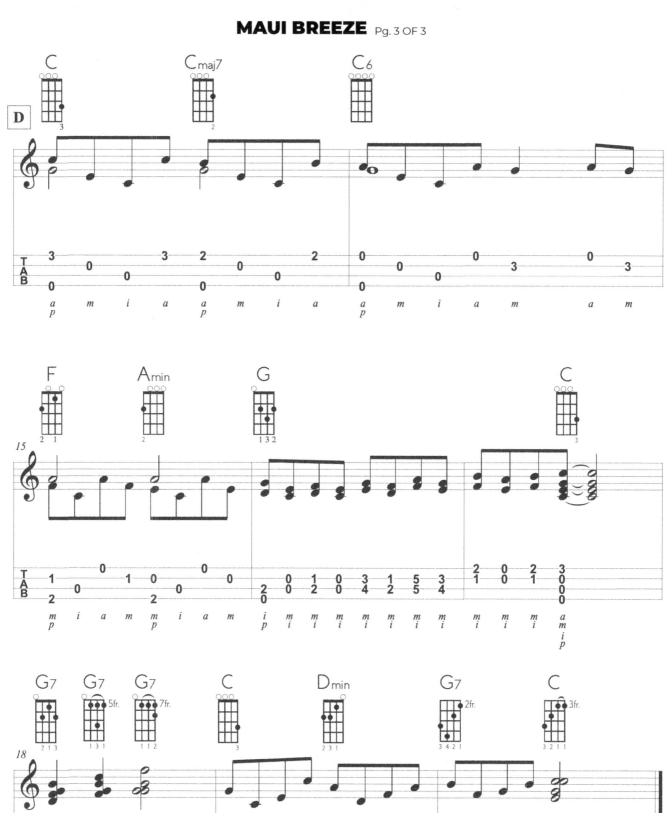

WHAT THE STUDENTS SAY:

"Literally was perfect. The videos were short but not too short. Kept my attention, gave me direction and practice but I could squeeze one in if I only had a few minutes.
The pacing was great.

The clarity was excellent in terms of being able to see what you're doing as well as your explanations. It was fun. I loved that we learned a little about the chords, the strumming and reading music. It was appropriately repetitive where needed but not too repetitive. It wasn't stressful but relaxing to made me want to put effort into getting better and remembering the chords.You're a great teacher!

And I'm a career educator and teacher evaluator by trade so I am a tough critic!"

Colleen Carroll

UKULELE STUDENT.

LESSON 11 GENTLE STROLL IN A MAJOR

This piece is in the key of A Major and in 3/4 time. Use the p-i-m-a-m-i fingerpattern throughout.

By Terry Carter

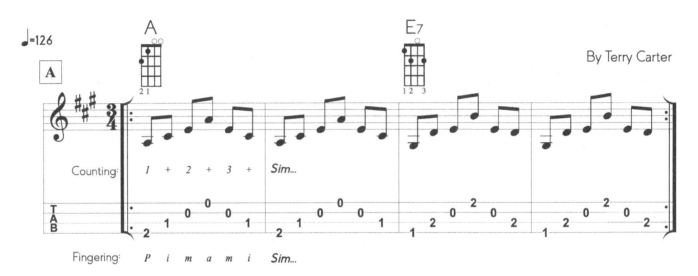

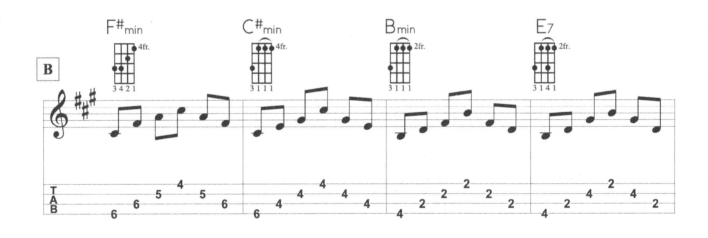

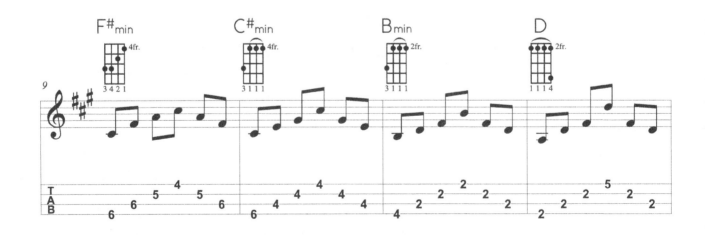

LESSON 12 FORBIDDEN ROAD IN D MINOR

This piece is in the key of D Minor and in 4/4 Time. Use the p-i-m-i fingerpattern throughout.

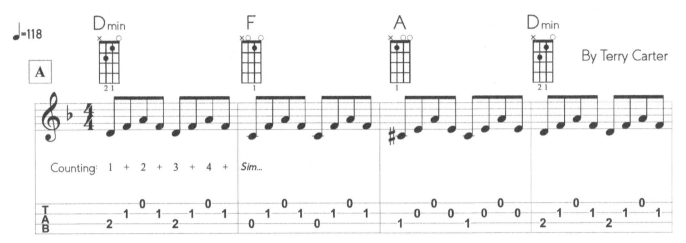

By Terry Carter

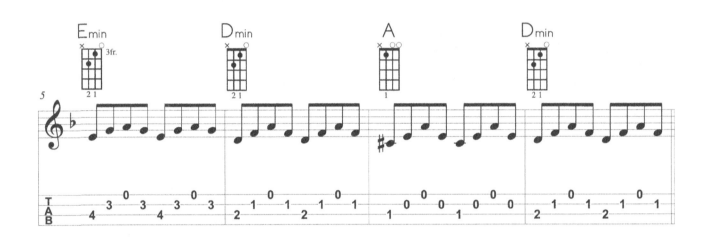

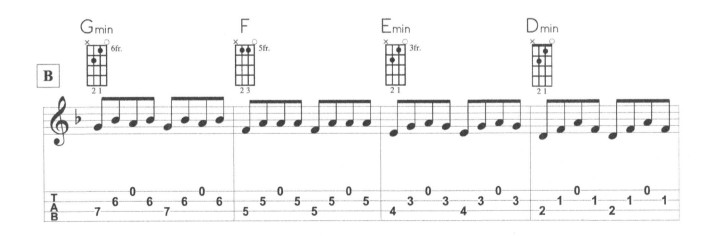

UKE LIKE THE PROS

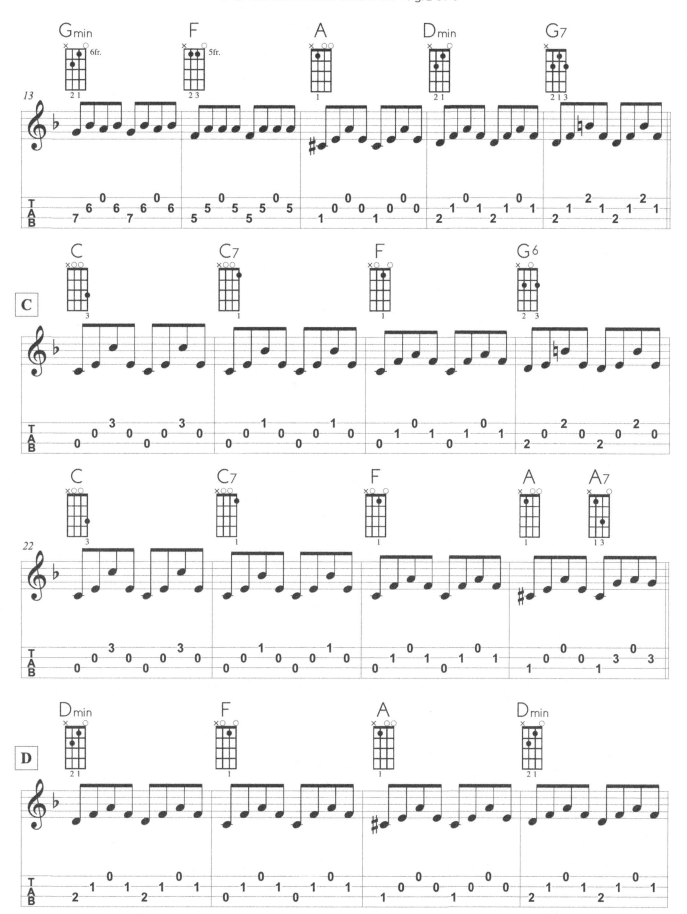

WHAT THE STUDENTS SAY:

"Being the person you are, you are able to inspire us all in your teachings just by being you. I feel very fortunate to have become one of your students, you are helping me to become a musician, maybe not the best, but the best I can become. I, like other members of ULTP I'm sure, look forward to what you have in store for us this year, hopefully we will inspire others to join us and realise their dreams to become musicians."

Peter Bailey
UKULELE STUDENT.

TRANGO TOWERS IN A MINOR

This piece is in the key of A Minor and uses pinches and backward rolls.

By Terry Carter

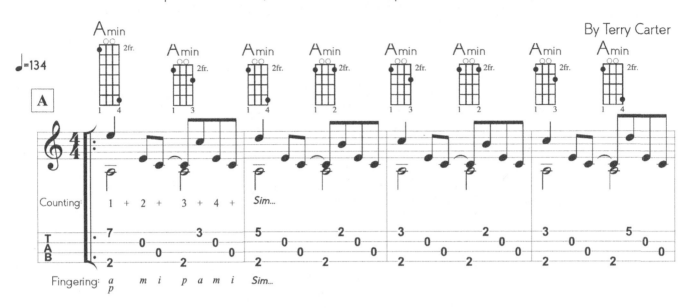

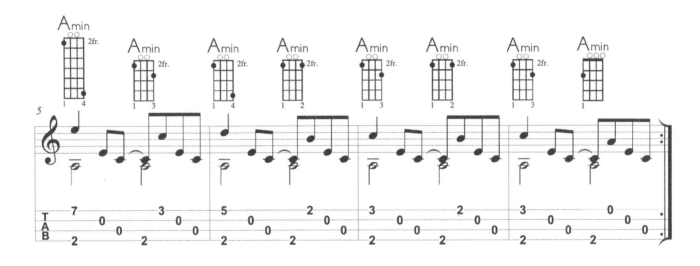

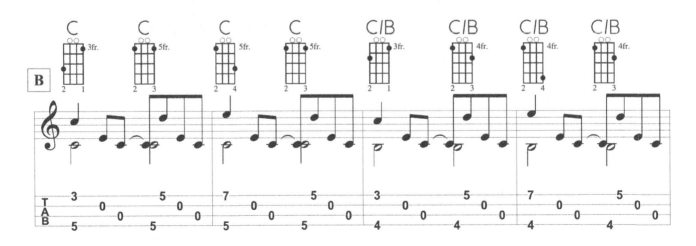

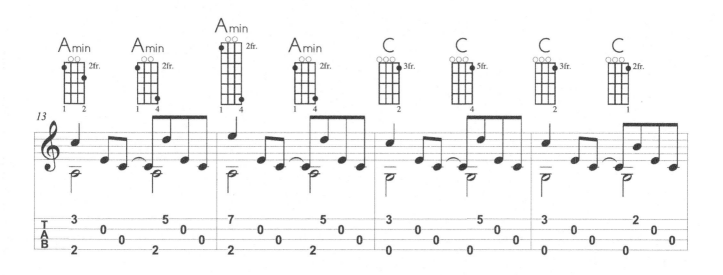

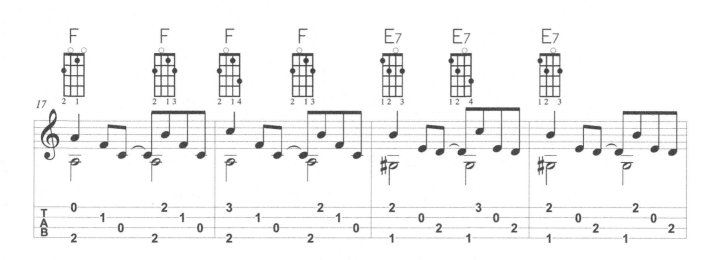

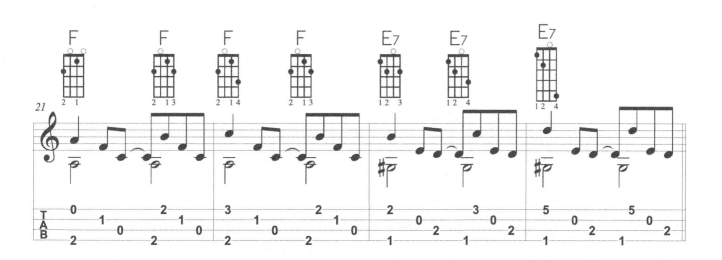

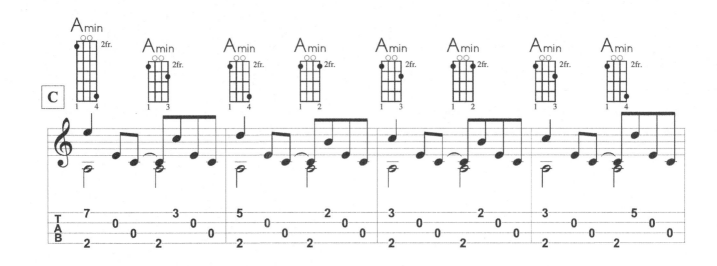

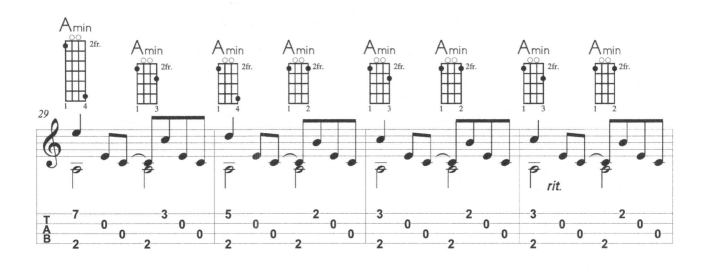

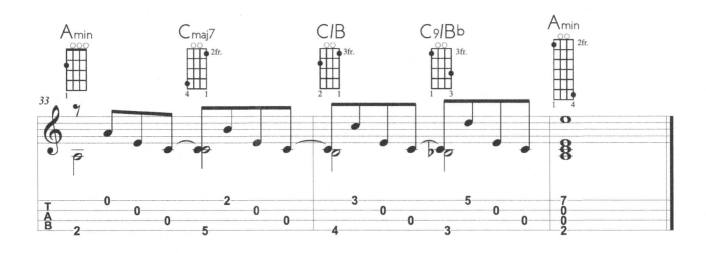

WHAT THE STUDENTS SAY:

"I am so glad I found your site! I probably spend at least 4 hours a day watching your lessons and practicing. I'm still at the beginning stage but it gives me a lot to look forward to.

I have spent a year jumping around on YouTube trying to find someone who could teach me how to play in a way that I could follow. I don't know how to read music but now I am learning.

You really are an amazing teacher and I truly appreciate your willingness to share your talents!"

Sue Lofgre

UKULELE STUDENT.

COAL'S BOOGIE IN A MAJOR

This is a Fingerstyle Blues in the key of A.

By Terry Carter

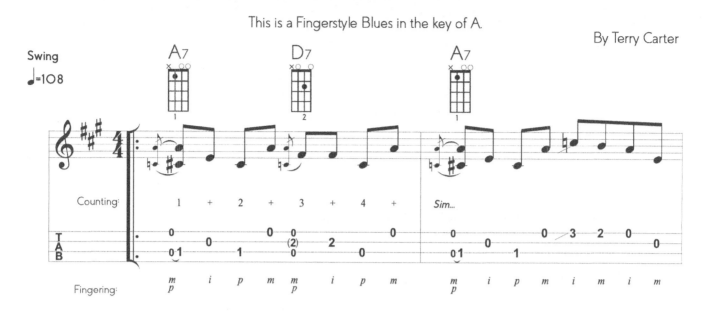

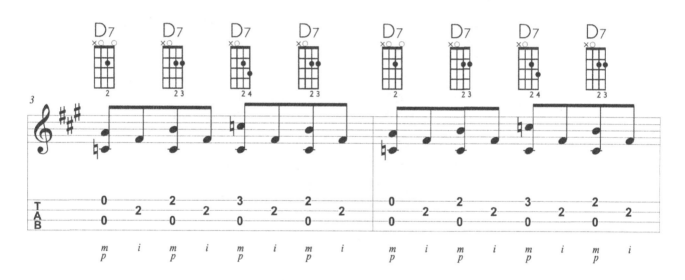

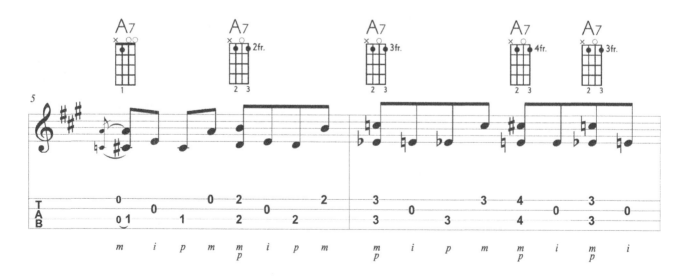

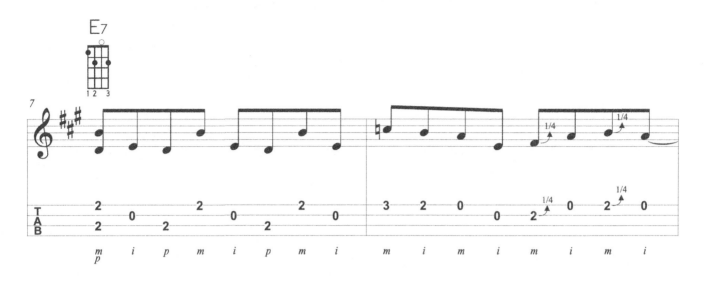

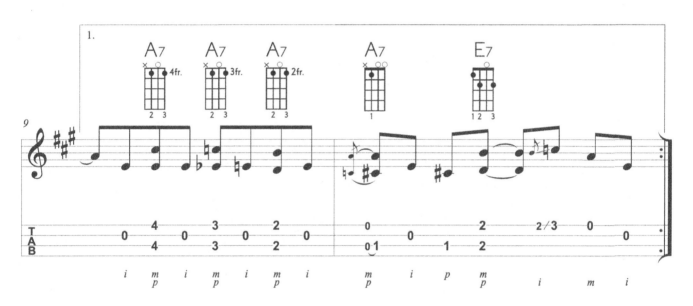

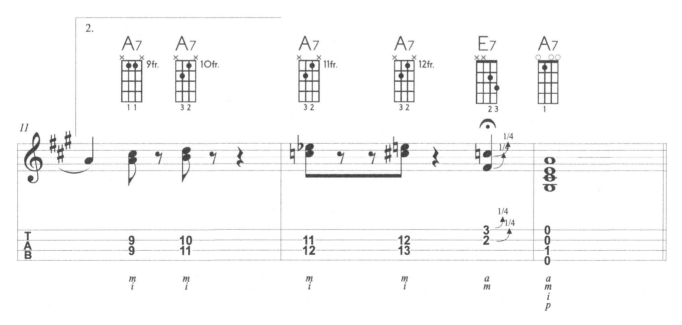

HAVANA TANGO

IN G MAJOR

This piece is in the key of G Major and uses pinches and backward rolls.

By Terry Carter

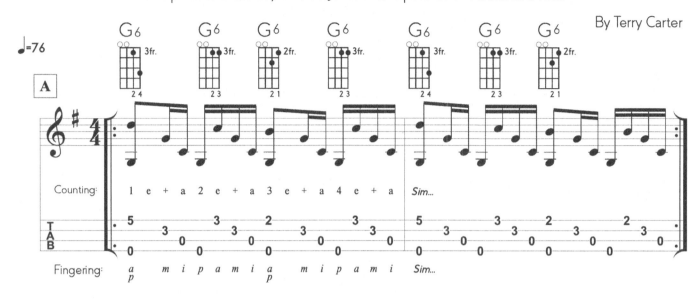

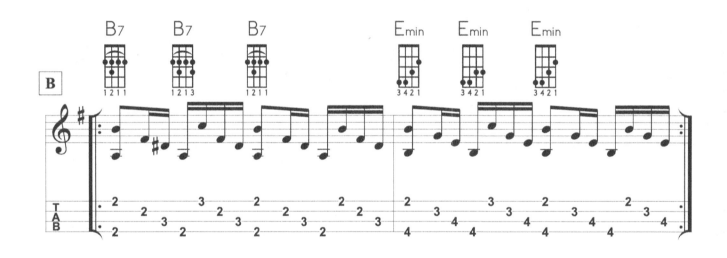

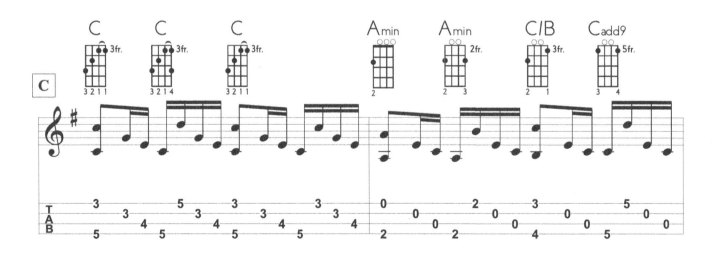

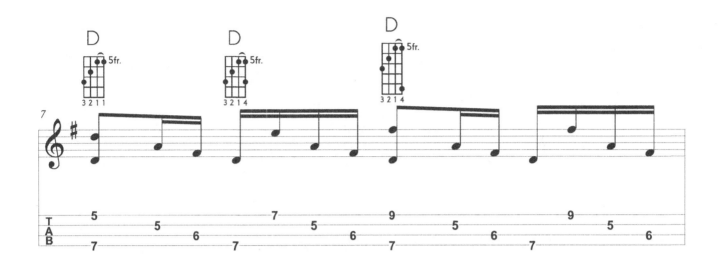

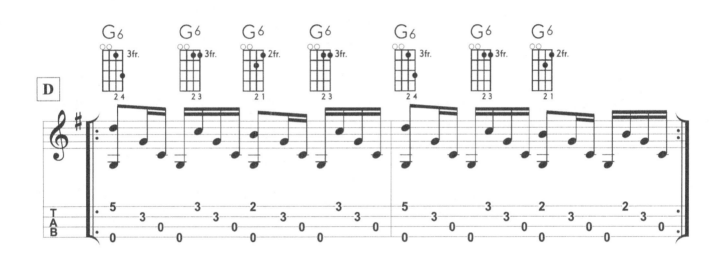

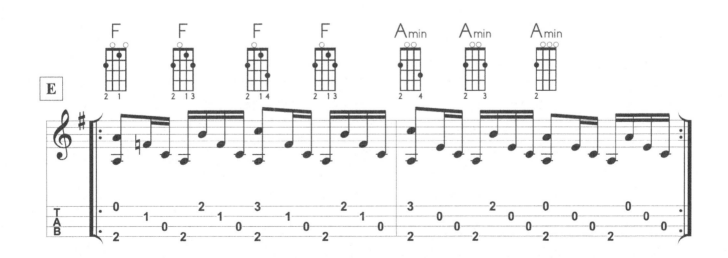

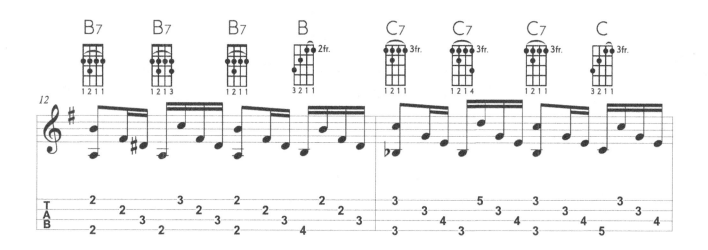

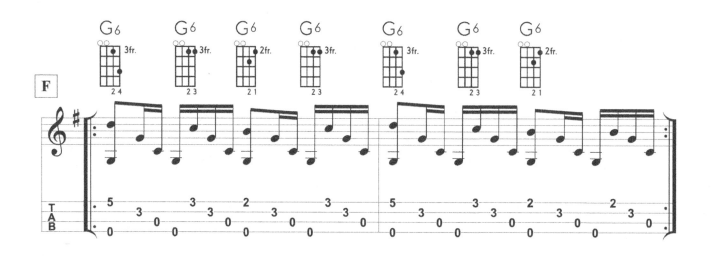

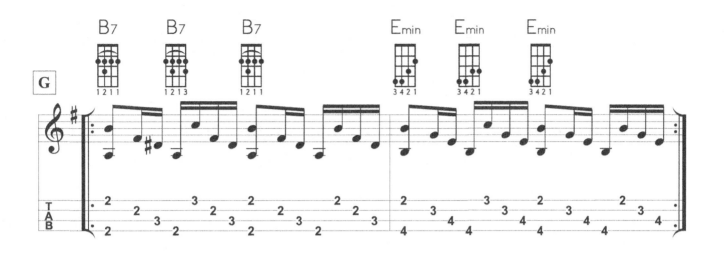

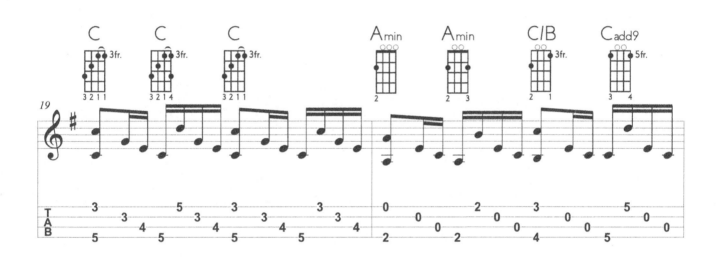

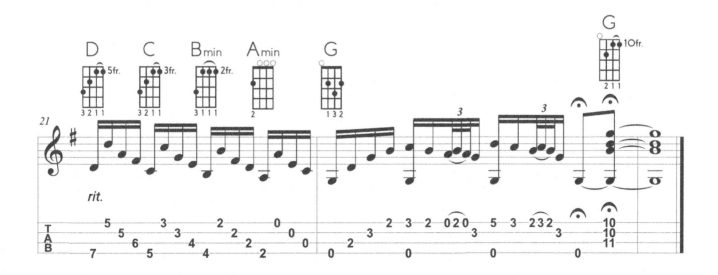

LESSON 16 **PHARAOH'S STONE** IN A MINOR

This piece is in the key of A Minor and uses tremolo with fingers a. m and i. Be sure
to tune the G string up a whole step to A.

By Terry Carter

Tune G String To A

♩=142

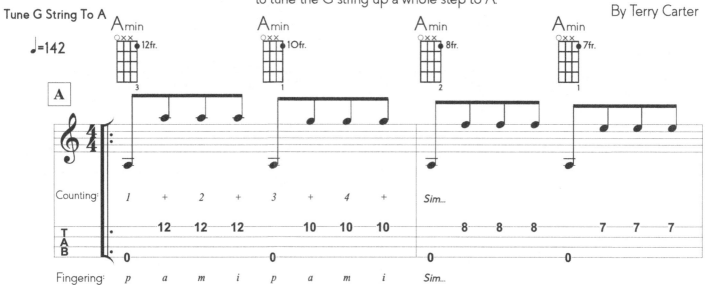

Counting: *1 + 2 + 3 + 4 + Sim...*

Fingering: *p a m i p a m i Sim...*

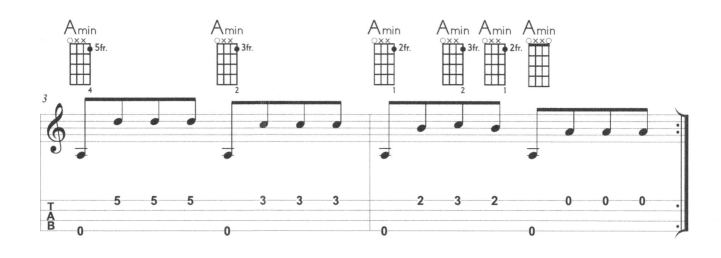

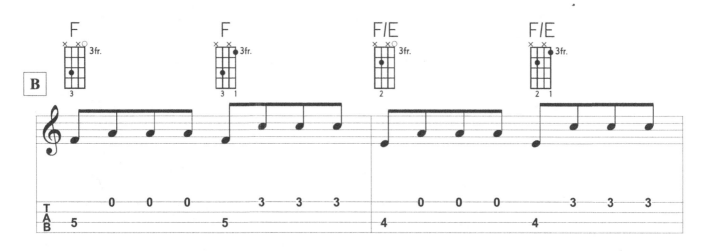

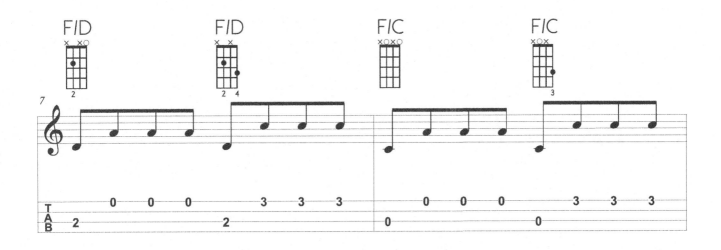

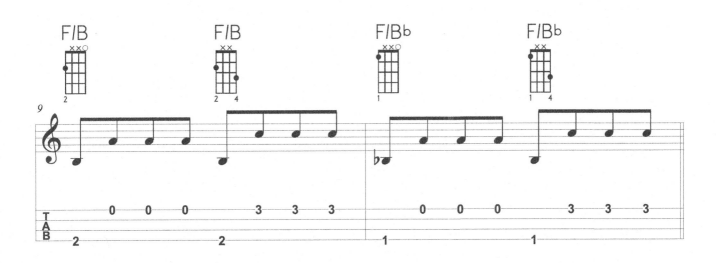

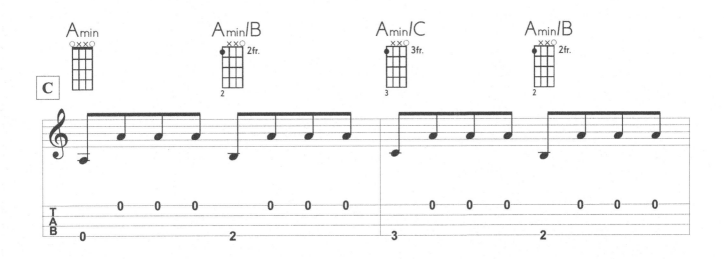

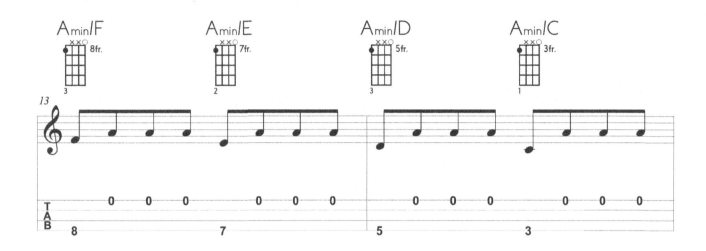

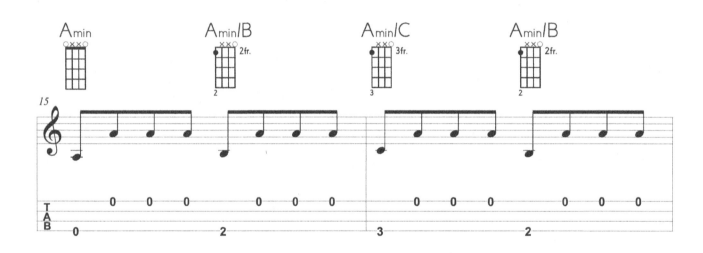

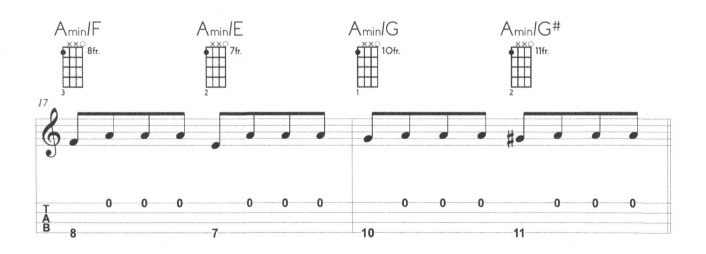

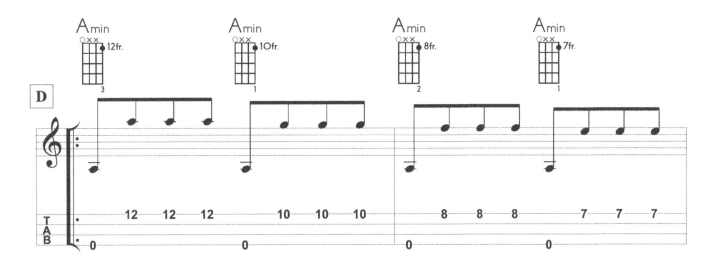

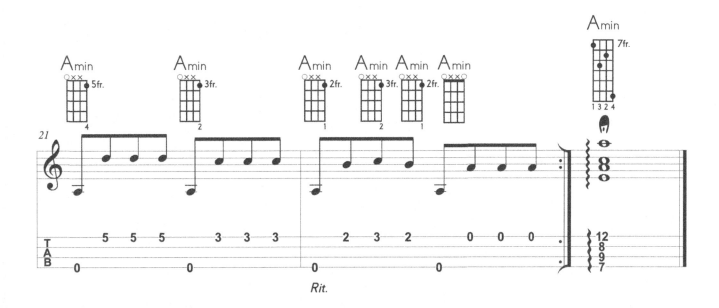

MIDNIGHT RENDEZVOUS

IN A MINOR

This piece is in A Minor. changes tempo in the C Section. and uses forward & backward rolls.

By Terry Carter

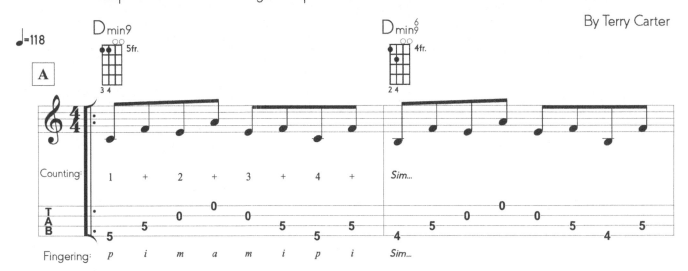

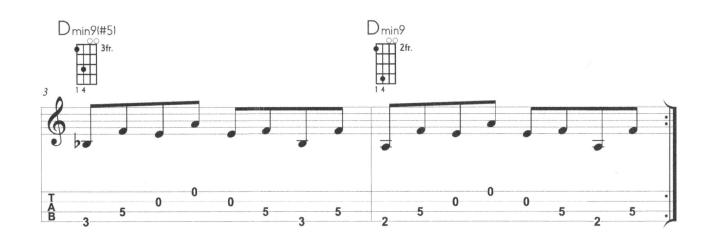

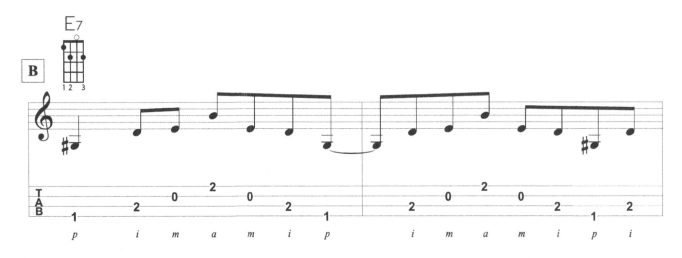

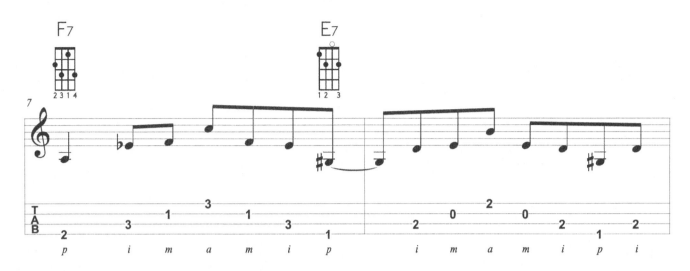

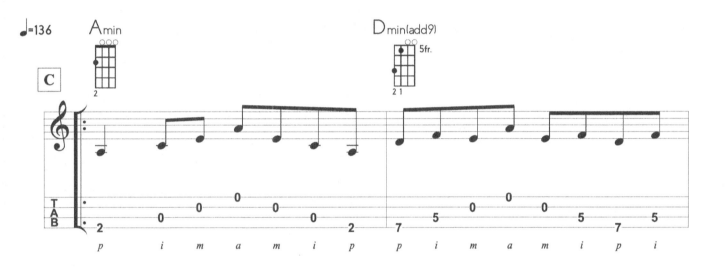

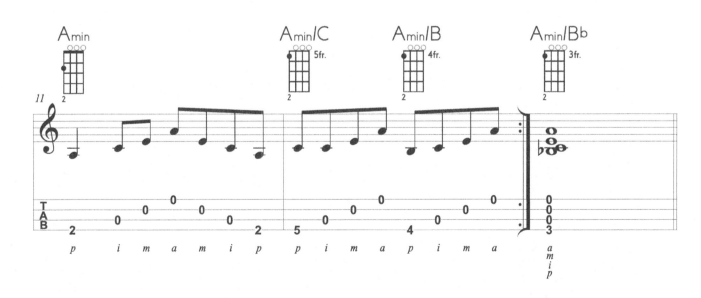

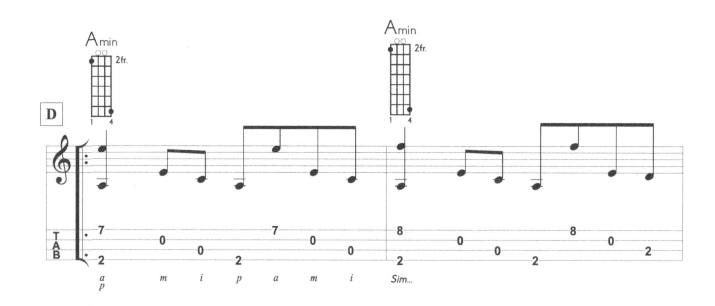

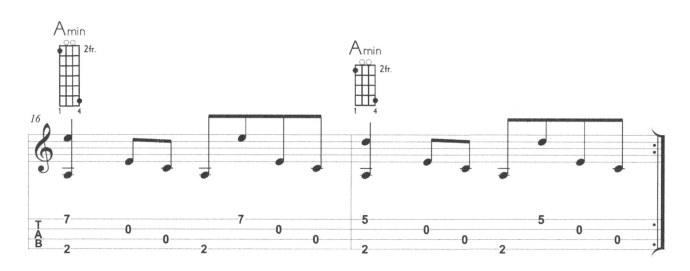

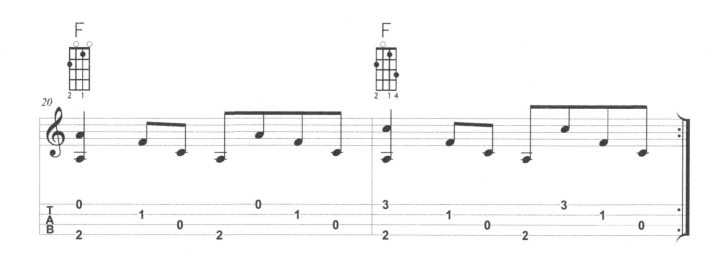

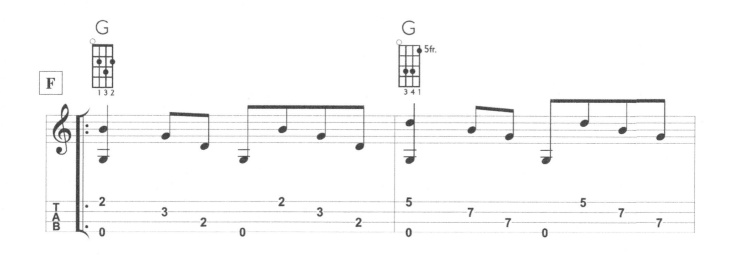

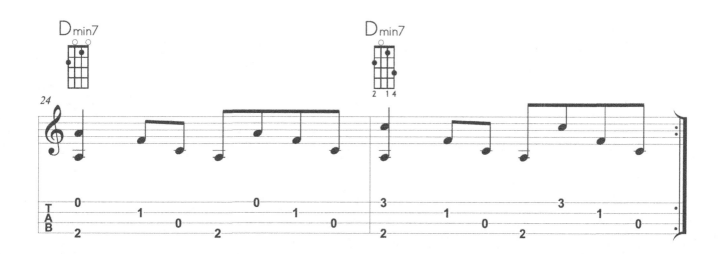

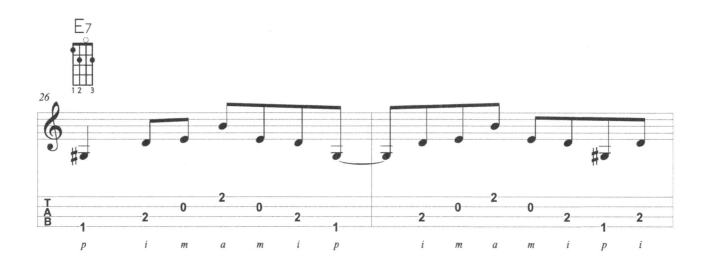

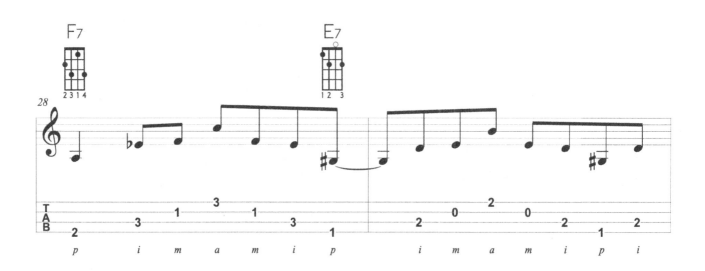

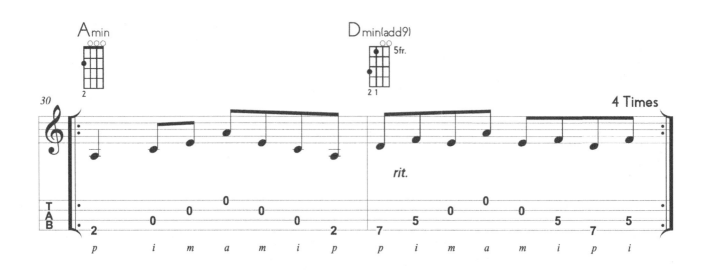

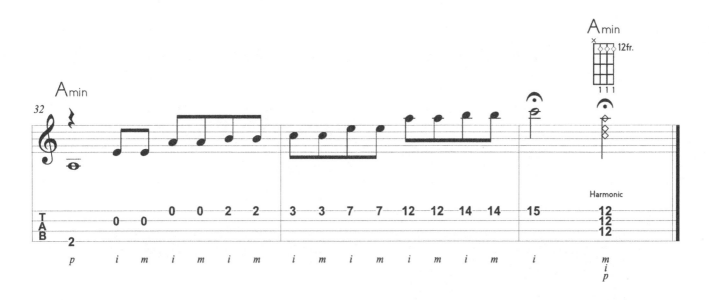

ABOUT THE AUTHOR

TERRY CARTER

Terry Carter is a San Diego-based ukulele player, surfer, songwriter, and creator of Uke Like The Pros and Rock Like The Pros. Terry has worked with Weezer, Josh Groban, Robby Krieger (The Doors), 2 time Grammy winner composer Christopher Tin (Calling All Dawns), and the Los Angeles Philharmonic. Terry has written and produced tracks for commercials (Puma and Discount Tire) and various television shows, including Scorpion (CBS), Pit Bulls & Parolees (Animal Planet), Trippin' and Wildboyz and The Real World (MTV). Terry received a Masters of Music in Studio/Jazz Guitar Performance from University of Southern California and a Bachelor of Music from San Diego State University, with an emphasis in Jazz Studies and Music Education.

ABOUT
UKELIKETHEPROS.COM

The perfect place to learn how to play Ukulele, Guitarlele or Baritone Ukulele.

Ukulele Beginning
Music Reading

Master the Ukulele 1

Guitarlele
For guitar and Ukulele
players

Ukulele Blues
Mastery

Baritone Blues
Mastery

Jazz Swing
Mastery

23 Ultimate Chord
Progressions Course

21 popular songs
for Ukulele

Baritone Ukulele
Bootcamp Course

ALL YOUR UKULELE NEEDS AT
store.**UKELIKE**THEPROS**.COM**

Ukuleles

Baritone Ukuleles

Guitarleles

Cases

Ukulele Books

Ukulele, Guitarlele,
and Baritone
ACCESORIES

UKELIKETHEPROS.COM
store.UKELIKETHEPROS.COM

@ukelikethepros

INTERESTED IN **GUITAR CONTENT?**

ROCKLIKETHEPROS.COM

Made in the USA
Columbia, SC
05 June 2021